HOLY COW! NOT ANOTHER MAD "SNAPPY ANSWERS to STUPID QUESTIONS" by Al Jaffee?

Written & Illustrated by Al Jaffee

Production by Joyce R. Jaffee

A Time Warner Company

WARNER BOOKS EDITION

For information address:
E.C. Publications, Inc.
485 Madison Avenue
New York, N.Y. 10022

Title "MAD" used with permission of its owner, E.C. Publications, Inc.

This Warner Books Edition is published by arrangement with E.C. Publications, Inc.

**Warner Books, Inc.
1271 Avenue of the Americas
New York, N.Y. 10020**

Printed in the United States of America

First Printing: December, 1992

10 9 8 7 6 5 4 3 2 1

SNAPPY ANSWERS
TO STUPID QUESTIONS

Are you going **outside?**

No, I **always dreamt** of becoming a **doorman** and I'm here to get some **practice.**
No, someone **left gum** on the **doorknob** and I **can't get my hand off.**
Oh, thank you for **reminding** me. I was **wondering** why I was standing here **dressed like this.**

Are you **stuck?**

No, I'm just resting. Everyone behind me is stuck.
No, my car died and I'm just trying to bury it.
No, the roads are too crowded so I decided to dig an underground highway just for me.

Something **wrong** with your **car?**

No, everything's **okay.** I'm just in here **installing** a **steam bath.**
No, I'm **discovering** why other cars **waste fuel. Their engines run.**
No, but there's **something wrong** with **me—for buying it.**

Is Raging Bull trying to **hurt** Machoman?
No, he's **studying** to be a **plastic surgeon** and he's **practicing** doing **nose jobs** now.
No, if he was trying to **hurt** him he'd be hitting something **other** than his **head**.
No, this is the **friendly** way wrestlers **greet** each other.

A SNAPPY ANSWERS TO STUPID QUESTIONS ARCHEOLOGICAL DIG

Are we going on an **archeological** expedition?

No, we've brought **twelve tons** of **digging equipment** along to build **giant sandcastles** on the beach.

Is this a **good** place to **dig?**
No, we've travelled **halfway around the world** to pick a place at **random.**

Is this the **tomb** of a **royal monarch?**
No, it's the **cashbox** of a **sleazy politician.**

Is that an **ancient oil lamp?**
No, it's a **brand new one** that somehow got **buried** in a **three thousand year old tomb.**

POOF

You have **one wish,** but it's a **good one. Anything you want you can have.**
Hate to **rush** you, master but I've got **another call** to make.
Is this **for real?** Is that a **Genii?** Are we **dreaming?** Am I **asking too many stupid questions?**
No...

. . . I just **wish** I was **so far away** I'd **never hear them again.**

Wish granted, master.

SNAPPY ANSWERS TO STUPID QUESTIONS THAT BACKFIRED

Do I **roll** the ball **toward** the pins?
No, the trick is to **kick it down the alley.**
12
13
14

Really? Show me!

Did you **catch** that in the **lake?**
No, I **trapped** it in the **woods.**

LOOKOUT! IT'S TRYING TO ESCAPE.

Does it say "WET PAINT"?
No, it says, "SIT DOWN".
PARK
PARK DEPT.
WET PAINT

Well then,
AGE BEFORE BEAUTY!
PARK
PARK DEPT
WET PAINT

Is there a way to **make sure** this medication is **SAFE?**
Yes. **Throw up before swallowing** it.

Like this?
WHOOPS!

Is **$5,000** what you **want** for this car?
No, **$25,000** is what I **want** for it. I wrote $5,000 just to get some **sucker interested.**
FOR SALE
$5,000.00

Oh, shucks. And all I had was this **measly check for $5,000.**

FOR SALE
$5,000.00

THROUGH HISTORY WITH SNAPPY ANSWERS TO STUPID QUESTIONS

FIRST LANDLADY TO FORBID PETS

FIRST MAGIC TRICK USING MIRRORS

FIRST DEBUTANTE COSTUME BALL

FIRST ANIMAL TO SAIL IN A REGATTA

FIRST CHILD INVITED TO A MASQUERADE PARTY

STINGING COMEBACKS TO SNAPPY ANSWERS TO STUPID QUESTIONS

How does it **look?**

Good if you **pull** the **collar over your ears.**

You mean the way **you'd look** if you **pulled your lip over your head?**

Is your child being **naughty?**
No, this is **how he is** when he's on his **best behavior.**
WAHH
PD

You must be
one helluva proud
role model.

Are these **donuts?**
No, they're **toilet seats** for **mini-butts** like **yours.**
PLAIN
SUGAR

Shucks, they look more like **head bands** for **mini-brains** like **yours.**

PLAIN

SUGAR

Is your house for sale?
No, the **fence** is.
17
FOR SALE

Good. It's certainly **more attractive** than that **dump behind it.**

FOR SALE

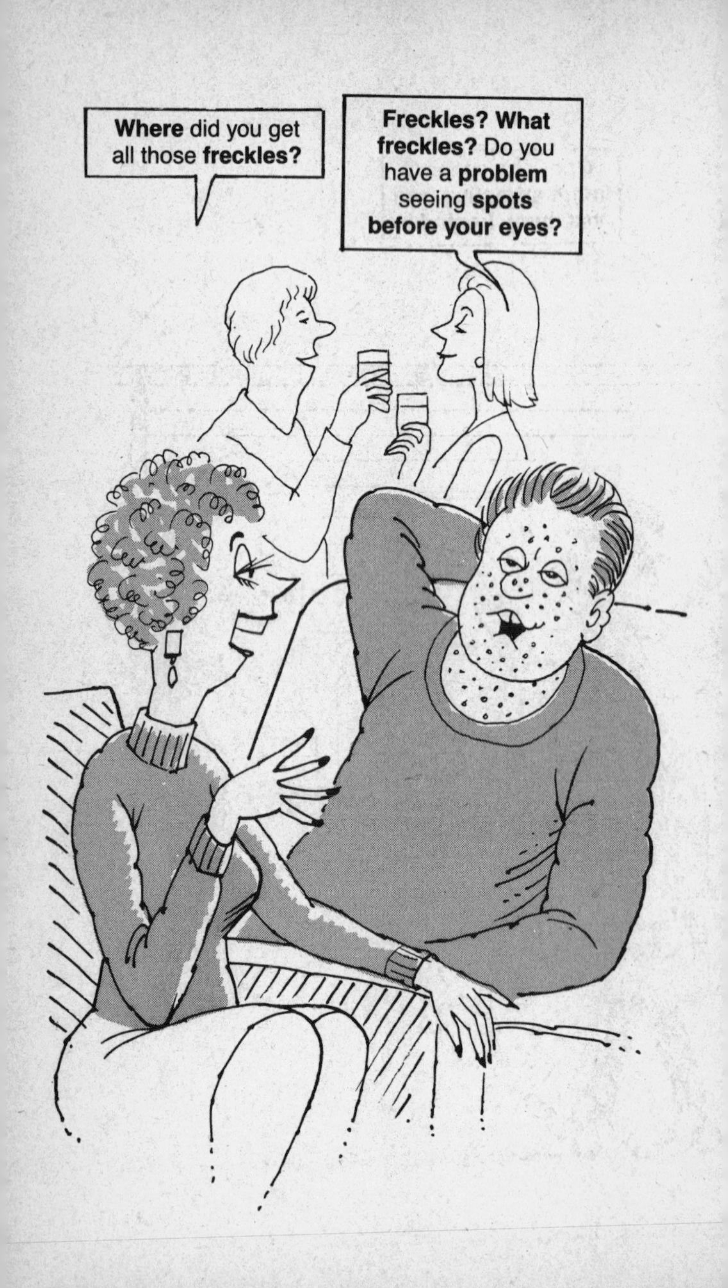
Where did you get all those freckles?
Freckles? What freckles? Do you have a problem seeing spots before your eyes?

No, I have a **problem** seeing **IDIOTS** **before my eyes.**

MORE SNAPPY ANSWERS TO STUPID QUESTIONS

Is there anyone **in the bathroom?**

Yes, the 82nd Airborne Division of the U.S. Air Force.
No, this is a recording. At the sound of the flush, please leave your message and get the hell out of here.
No, but it's been condemned as a toxic waste dump and no one's allowed in.

Do you feel cold?

No, not since **rigor mortis** set in.
C-c-cold? H-h-how could I feel cold? This box is made of **t-t-two layers** of **c-c-cardboard.**
N-n-no. I'm just **t-t-tap dancing** with m-m-my **t-t-teeth.**

Am I late for my date with Penny, Mrs. Jones?

No, you're **early** if it's **breakfast** you had in mind.
No, not if you **enjoy watching** someone **sleep soundly.**
No, you'll **find her** in the living room **under a pile of cobwebs.**

Is this **where** we get our **luggage?**

CHAPTER 11 AIRLINE
BAGGAGE
CLAIM AREA

No, this is **where** we get our **heart attacks** as we watch every bag **except ours** appear.
No, this is **free** airline entertainment to **make up for** the **lousy chopped up** inflight **movie.**
No, this is **where** we **wait** and **wait** until we hear the **loudspeaker announce** that **our** baggage is being unloaded in the terminal at the **other end of the airport.**

A SNAPPY ANSWERS TO STUPID QUESTIONS SEA SAGA

Our engine's quit. What now?
GIVE THANKS IT'S NOT WORSE.

Our radio's shot.
What now?
GIVE THANKS
IT'S NOT WORSE.

A storm's coming up.
What now?

GIVE THANKS
IT'S NOT WORSE.

Boat's breaking up. What now?

GIVE THANKS IT'S NOT WORSE.

We're surrounded by sharks. What now?

GIVE THANKS IT'S NOT WORSE.

We've been drifting for a month with no rescue in sight. What now?
GIVE THANKS IT'S NOT WORSE.

I CAN'T STAND IT ANY MORE. WE'RE IN TERRIBLE TROUBLE AND ALL YOU KEEP SAYING IS, "GIVE THANKS IT'S NOT WORSE. GIVE THANKS IT'S NOT WORSE".

WELL, IT IS WORSE. MUCH WORSE!

THERE'S ONLY ONE DRINK OF WATER LEFT...

L'EAU

...AND I'M GOING TO DRINK IT.

AGUA

THANKS!

WASSER

MORE SNAPPY ANSWERS TO STUPID QUESTIONS THAT BACKFIRED

Is the food good here?
No, but happily the portions are small.
RESTAURANT

And so are your **profits,** I'm sure.
RESTAURANT

Are you **shaving?**
No, my **jaw's too big** so I'm **shrinking** it with **vanishing cream.**

Here! Try some where you need it most.
SHAVING
FOAM

Are you **trying to walk** with those **crutches?**
No, I'm **trying to do the Polka** the **hard way.**

Let me **help**!
A one and a two...
A one and a two...

Putting up an **antenna?**
No, I'm **building** a **nest** so I can spend the **rest of my life** up here **free** as a **bird.**

POOF! I'm your Fairy Godmother and I've just granted your wish.

Is your book for sale?
No, it's here so you can read it for free.
BOOK SALE TODAY MEET THE AUTHOR

Sorry, but I **don't like to do things** that make me **BARF** in public.
BOOK SALE TODAY MEET THE AUTHOR

STILL MORE SNAPPY ANSWERS TO STUPID QUESTIONS

Who made this **mess?**

I did but it was an accident. I accidentally picked up all my toys and I accidentally threw them all over the room.
Hey Mickey, stand up when Mommy's talking to you.
You mean you don't know about the earthquake that ran through this end of the house?

Working **hard?**

No, this is the posh PICK AND SHOVEL COUNTRY CLUB.
No, my tools do the hard work. I just supervise.
Work? This? Oh NO! Golfing is work. Tennis is work. Bowling is work. This? This is pure relaxation.

Do you carry
foreign videos?
FOREIGN
VIDEOS

No, I **leave** them **right there** on the **shelf.**
No, these are all **imported domestic** videos.
To people from **your planet** they certainly **will be** foreign.

Are you guys **truck drivers?**
T.,J.,&J.
REVEN
LONG DIS
MOVING & ST

DYSPEPTIC
DINER
No, we're the Nobel Prize committee meeting to pick this year's winners.
No, we're the President's cabinet traveling incognito.
No, we're transplant surgeons here to pick up organs for today's operations.

MORE STINGING COMEBACKS TO SNAPPY ANSWERS TO STUPID QUESTIONS

Are you going to wear those **earphones?**
No, I'm going to **stuff** them into my **ear cavity.**

Try your **brain cavity.** There's **much more empty space there.**

Family pictures?
No, for a **change** I thought I'd **display total strangers.**

Smart idea. I've **seen** your family.

Do you want me to **take out the garbage?**
No, **leave** it here **all winter** to **grow worms** for your spring **fishing trip.**

No need. I use **your leftovers** for that.

Are you a **professional clown?**
No, I just dress this way **for laughs.**

You might get **more** of them **without** the makeup!

HELP
What's **new?**
I've been **arrested** for **loitering.**

Oh my God. It's happening. I'm cracking up. I've been on this forsaken island so long I'm starting to have conversations with an idiotic figment of my imagination.
HELP

MORE THROUGH HISTORY WITH SNAPPY ANSWERS TO STUPID QUESTIONS

FIRST FOOD CRISIS IN THE U.S.A.

FIRST AFTER DINNER JOKE

FIRST MANNED ROCKET SHIP

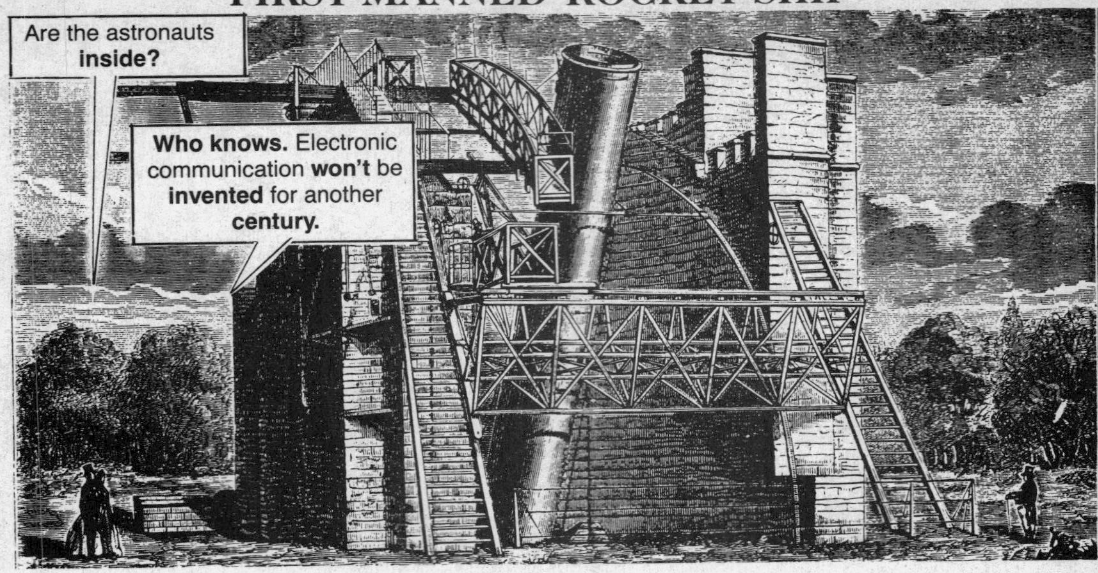

FIRST HUMANE ANIMAL SHELTER

FIRST TEAM TO PLAY NIGHT BASEBALL

ONCE MORE WITH SNAPPY ANSWERS TO STUPID QUESTIONS

Do you **live** here?

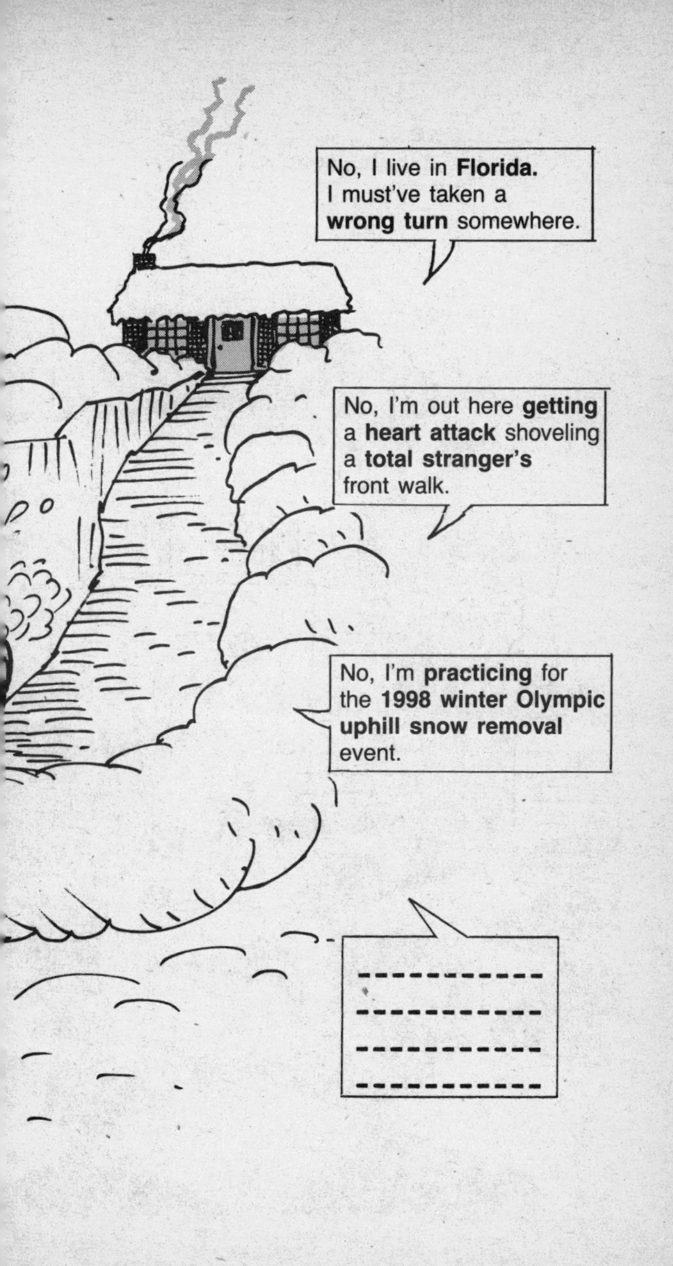
No, I live in **Florida.** I must've taken a **wrong turn** somewhere.
No, I'm out here **getting** a **heart attack** shoveling a **total stranger's** front walk.
No, I'm **practicing** for the **1998 winter Olympic uphill snow removal** event.

Are you doing **housework?**
AJA

No, I'm doing a **new form** of **aerobics.**
No, I'm **nearsighted** and the only way I can **play chess** is on this **giant board.**
No, I'm into a new hobby called "**DRUDGERY FOR FUN AND PROFIT**".

Are you on **vacation?**
Hotel
BigBucks
SUN

No, I'm working. My job is testing beach chairs.
No, I'm homeless and the kind folks who own this hotel are letting me stay in the penthouse suite till I get back on my feet again.
No, all my clothes were stolen and this is the only place I can hang out without looking conspicuous.
SUN GOO

Are wrestling fans ever upset by excessive brutality?

YAWN
Yes, if there's **not enough** of it.
Only when it's **less** than **they get at home.**
Not if they get a chance to **participate** in it.

STILL MORE SNAPPY ANSWERS TO STUPID QUESTIONS THAT BACKFIRED

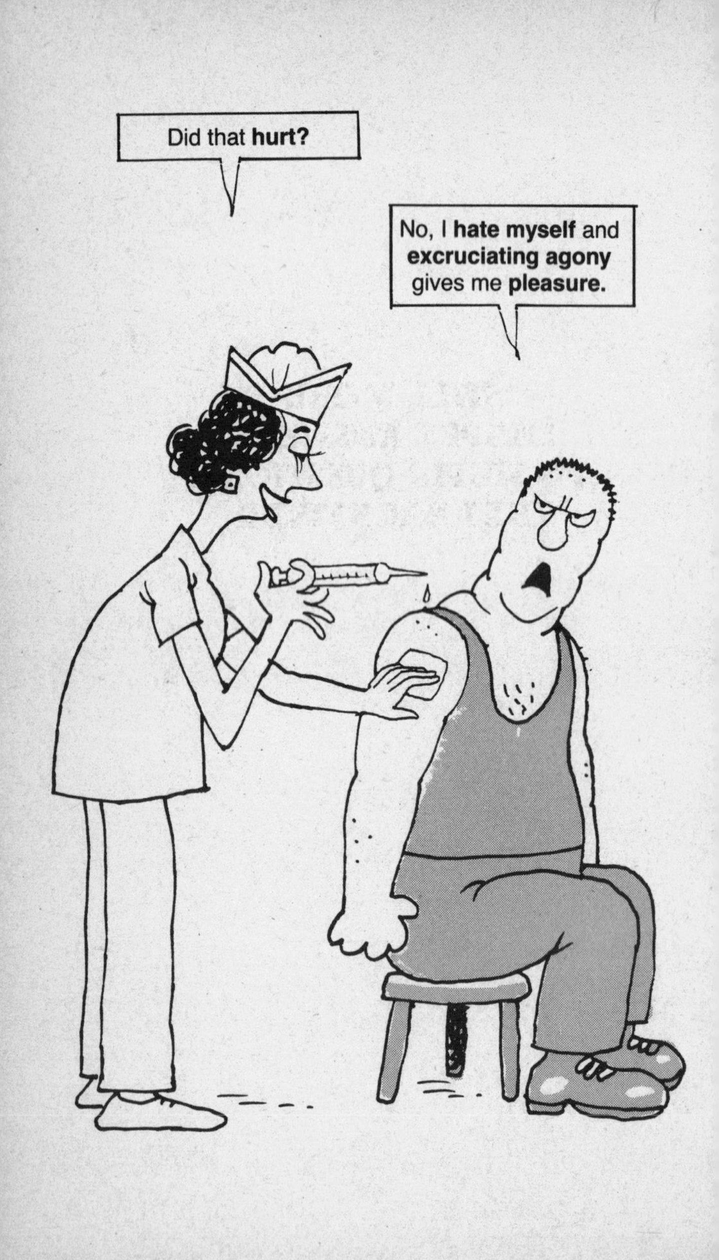
Did that **hurt?**
No, I **hate myself** and **excruciating agony** gives me **pleasure.**

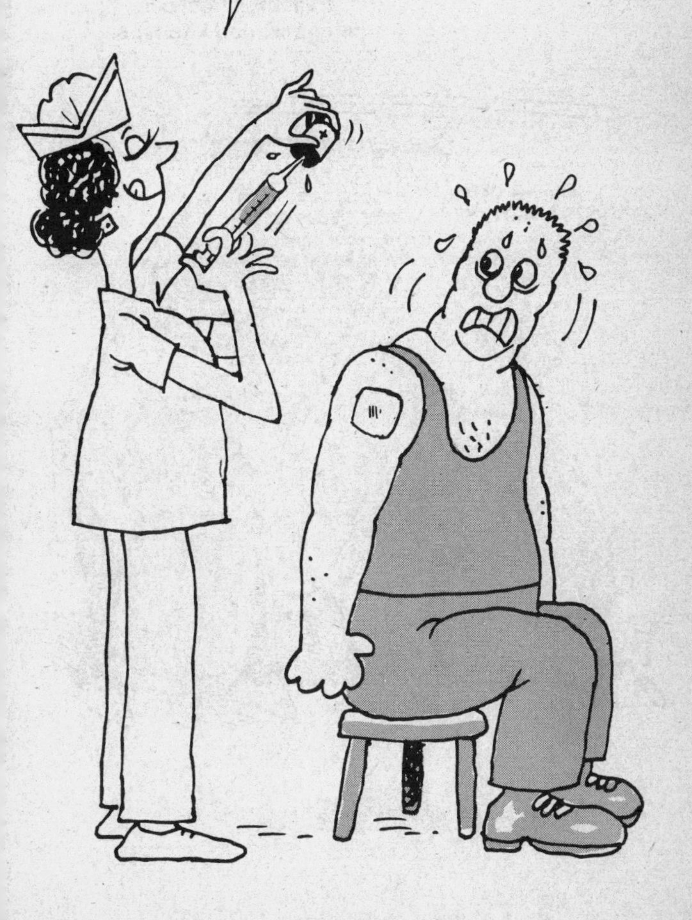
Oh, then you'll **love** it that I made a **mistake** and have to "**shoot**" you **all over again.**

Are you collecting **garbage?**

No, I'm collecting **antiques.** Antique **potato skins, egg shells,** and other **treasures** from our **neighborhood kitchens.**
SANITATION

These **ancient fish entrails** should **make your day.**
ITATION

Got a **leak?**
No, I punched a **hole** in the **bottom** so I could see **how deep** it is here.

Take a closer look.

Are you busy **typing,** Miss Frumprump?
No, I'm **playing** a **concerto** on this **cute little piano.**

Wonderful. For an encore here's a symphony in 38 movements you can enjoy far into the night.

Lose something?
Yes, **MY MIND.** Why **else** would I **crawl around like this?**

20 20
Whew! For a moment there I was afraid you were looking for this twenty I just found.
20 20

A SNAPPY ANSWERS TO STUPID QUESTIONS WAR STORY

Was it **bad out there,** kid?

BAD? What could be bad? Staying alive is NOT the most important thing in life, y'know.
No, it was great. You really should try it. It's certainly better than sitting around in the Officer's Club getting fat and lazy.
DRANO
Heavens no! I was always embarrassed about being UNDERWEIGHT and now with all this lead in me . . .

STILL MORE STINGING COMEBACKS TO SNAPPY ANSWERS TO STUPID QUESTIONS

Are you the **driver?**
No, I'm one of the **passengers.** The driver likes to **sit in the back of the bus** where there's **peace** and **quiet.**
SANTA ROSA-MORGAN & WYATT

Swell. Then he won't **hear me** when I tell you this bus company **hires** nothing but **rude imbeciles** and **boors.**
SANTA ROSA-MORGAN & WYATT

Did you go **bowling?**
No, someone spilled **Krazy Glue** in the holes and now my **fingers** are **stuck forever.**

Too bad you didn't put your tongue in.

Been out **grocery** **shopping?**
No, I've been out **rummaging** through **garbage** containers.
FLAKO

Oh, no! Not THAT for dinner again!
FLAKO

Is that your **wife**, Sir?
No, it's a **water buffalo I trained** to do **housework.**
AVON

Amazing. One stupid beast trains another.

Anyone in the audience have a **comment?**
BULL CRAP!

The chair **recognizes** **Mr. Bull Crap.**

Are you yawning?
No, these are mouth stretching exercises in case I ever have to swallow a whale.
OPERA
OPERA

You mean **ONE** isn't **enough** for you?
OPERA
OPERA

ONCE AGAIN WITH SNAPPY ANSWERS TO STUPID QUESTIONS THAT BACKFIRED

Is this **too loud**, Sir?
What? What? Some **idiot** is playing a **boombox so loud I CAN'T HEAR!**
FANI IS TOPS
JESSE WINS

CAN'T HEAR? Okay I'll turn it WAY UP!
FANI IS TOPS
JESSE WINS

Do you carry **Indian pottery?**
No, **I SELL 'um. You CARRY 'um.**
NATIVE AMERICAN CRAFTS

No, I LEAVE 'um. you SHOVE 'um.
NATIVE AMERICAN CRAFTS

I'm sorry. Did I **hurt you?**
No, my **shoe's too big** and now the **swelling** makes it **fit perfectly.**
POP

Okay. How about a **matched set?**
Pop

Raising **tomatoes?**

No, **soccer balls.**

GOAL!!

Am I **too fat**, Doc?
Too fat for **what?**
293

Too fat to lean over your desk and write out a check for the visit.
293

FINALLY THE LAST OF SNAPPY ANSWERS TO STUPID QUESTIONS

GYM
Are you **training** for a **fight?**
EVERPUNCHY
S.G.

No, I'm **preparing** to become a **subway commuter.**
No, I'm learning to **knead dough** so I can get a **job** at **Pizza Hut.**
No, I'm practicing for my **next encounter** with an idiot **who asks stupid questions.**

Is it **lunch** time?

No, it's **game** time. If you can **identify** what's on the tray you **win** and don't have to **eat** it.
No, we're **testing** to see **how many rows** can be jammed in and still leave **enough room** for a **food tray** on your **lap.**
No, it's **self control** time to find out **how long** you can **wait** when food carts block the aisles to the **bathrooms for hours.**

Do you have a **cold?**
AH

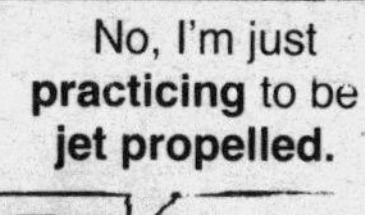
No, I'm just practicing to be jet propelled.
CHOO
No, I'm creating lyrics for a new type of rap music.
No, I swallowed some firecrackers and they go off in my stomach every now and then.

Are you **drunk?**
YECCH

I certainly hope so. I (hic) don't see creatures like you when I'm sober.
No, YOU must be. Otherwise (hic) you wouldn't be tilted while I'm standing straight up.
WANTED
NOT!
No, and I wish you two would stop asking (hic) such stupid questions.

Other books
by Mad's (yecch!)
Al Jaffee

MAD's Al Jaffee Spews Out SNAPPY ANSWERS TO STUPID QUESTIONS (#1)

MAD's Al Jaffee Spews Out MORE SNAPPY ANSWERS TO STUPID QUESTIONS (#2)

Good Lord! Not Another Book of SNAPPY ANSWERS TO STUPID QUESTIONS by MAD's (Yecch!) Al Jaffee (#3)

MAD's Al Jaffee Spews Out STILL MORE SNAPPY ANSWERS TO STUPID QUESTIONS (#4)

SNAPPY ANSWERS TO STUPID QUESTIONS #5 by MAD's Al Jaffee (#5)

Once Again MAD's Al Jaffee Spews Out "SNAPPY ANSWERS TO STUPID QUESTIONS" (#6)

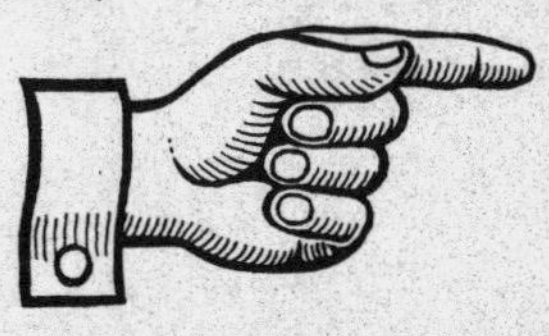

MAD's ALL NEW "SNAPPY ANSWERS TO STUPID QUESTIONS by Al Jaffee"(#7)

Al Jaffee's MAD (Yecch!) MONSTROSITIES

Al Jaffee's MAD BOOK OF MAGIC AND OTHER DIRTY TRICKS

Al Jaffee's MAD INVENTIONS

MAD's Al Jaffee FREAKS OUT

MAD BRAIN TICKLERS, PUZZLERS, AND LOUSY JOKES by Al Jaffee

MAD's Al Jaffee SWEATS OUT ANOTHER BOOK

Al Jaffee'S MAD (Yecch!) REJECTS